Dinn

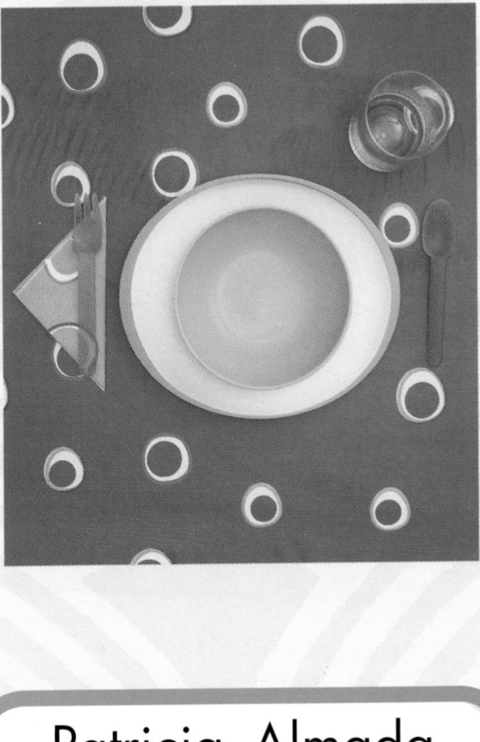

Patricia Almada

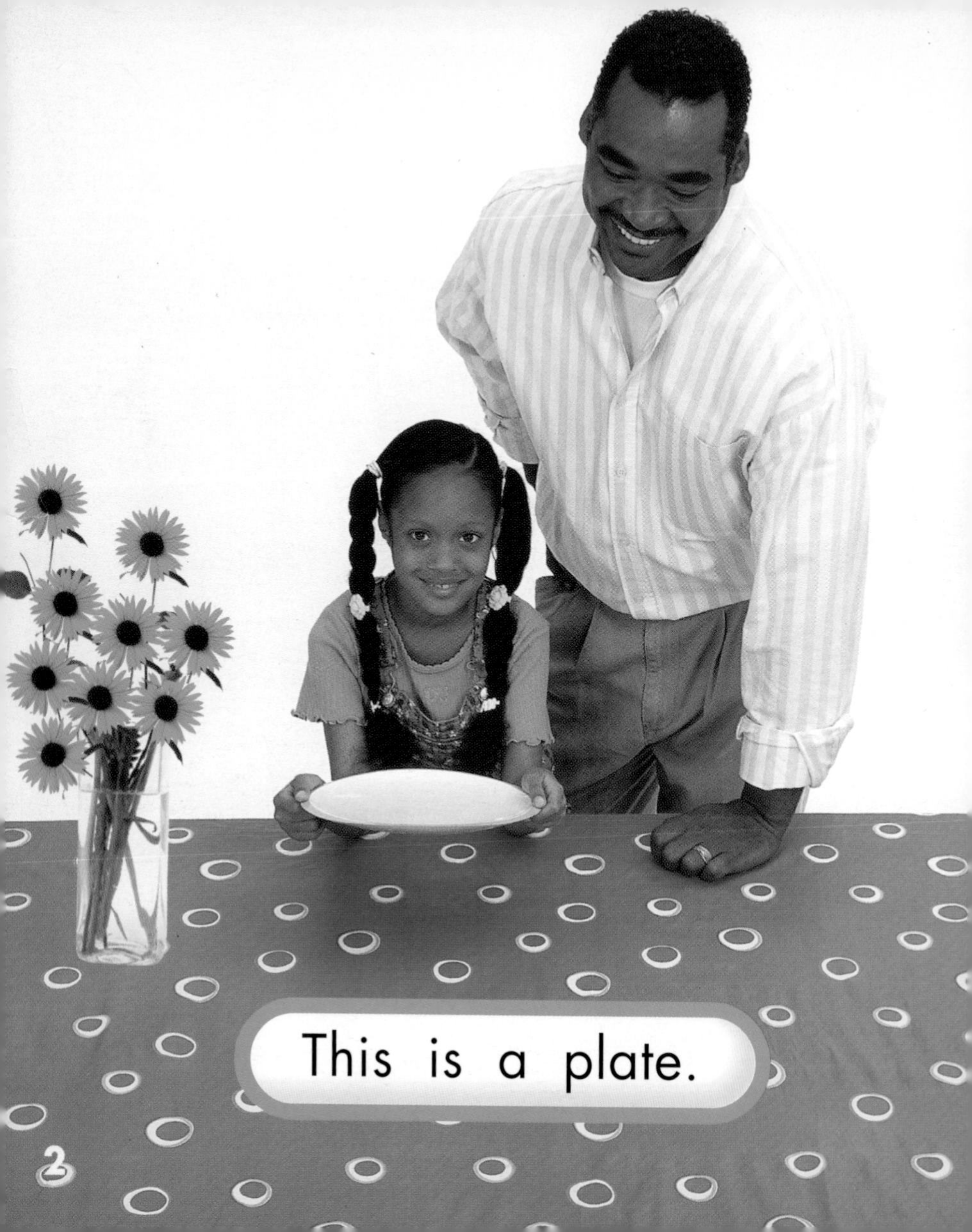

This is a plate.

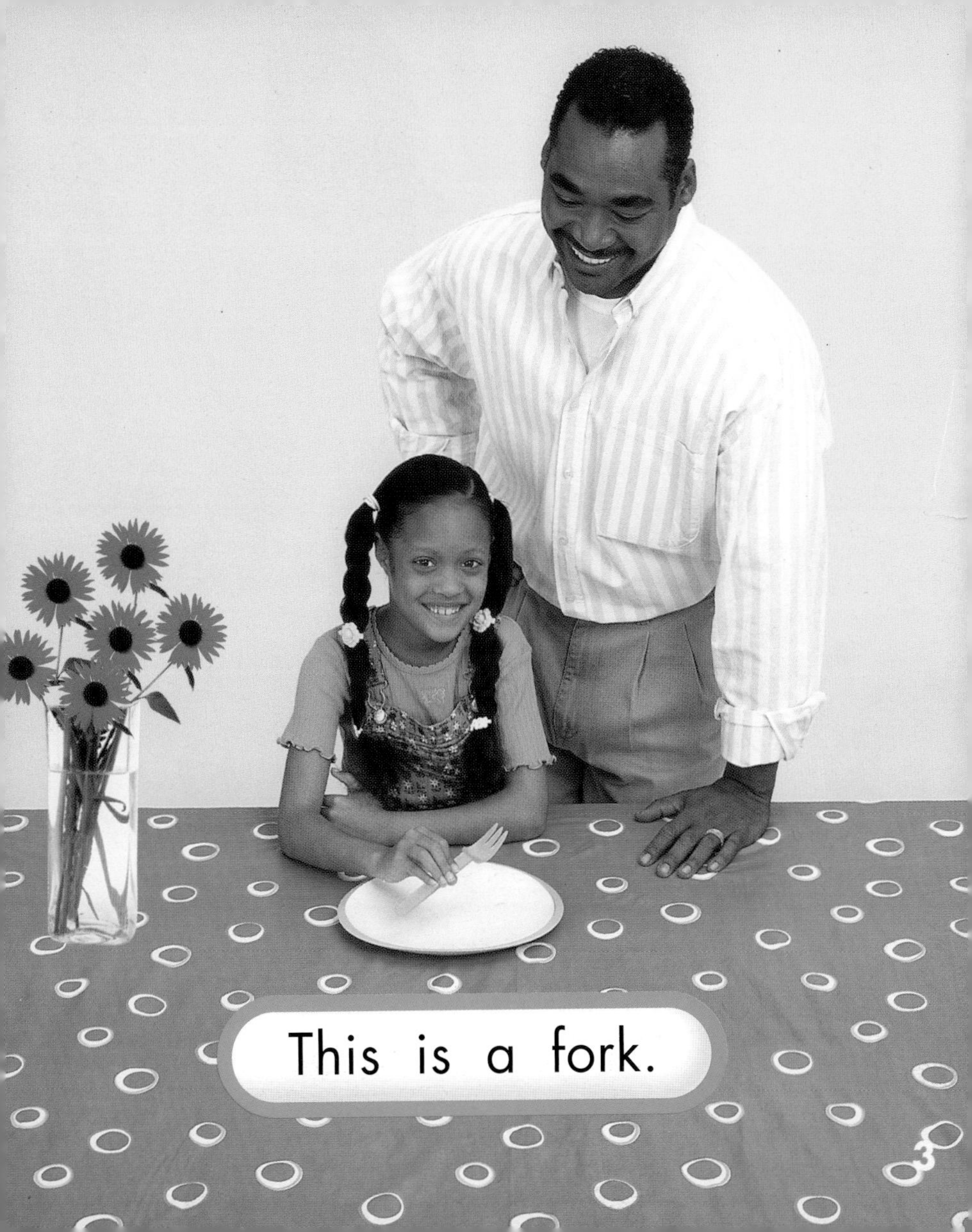

This is a fork.

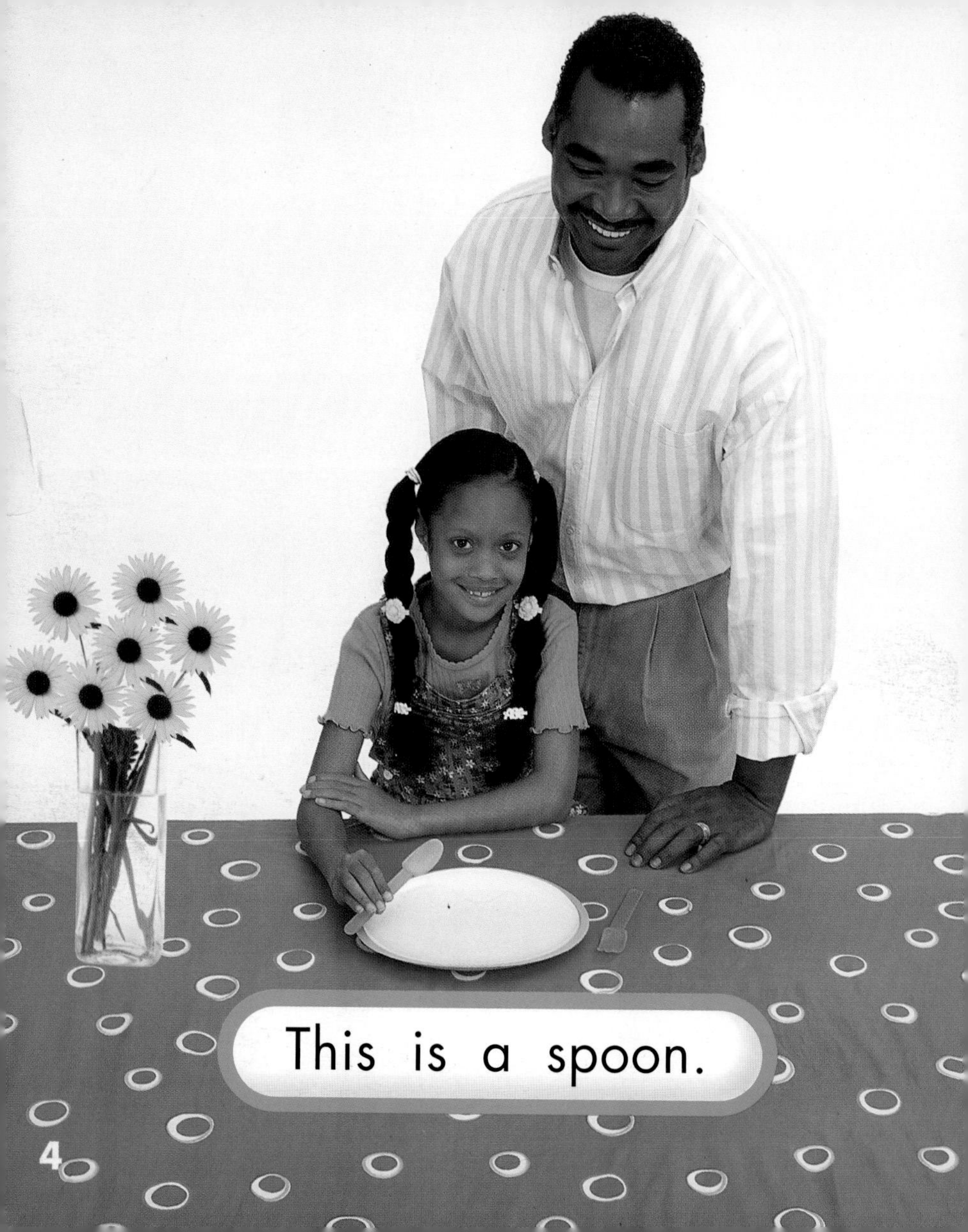

This is a spoon.

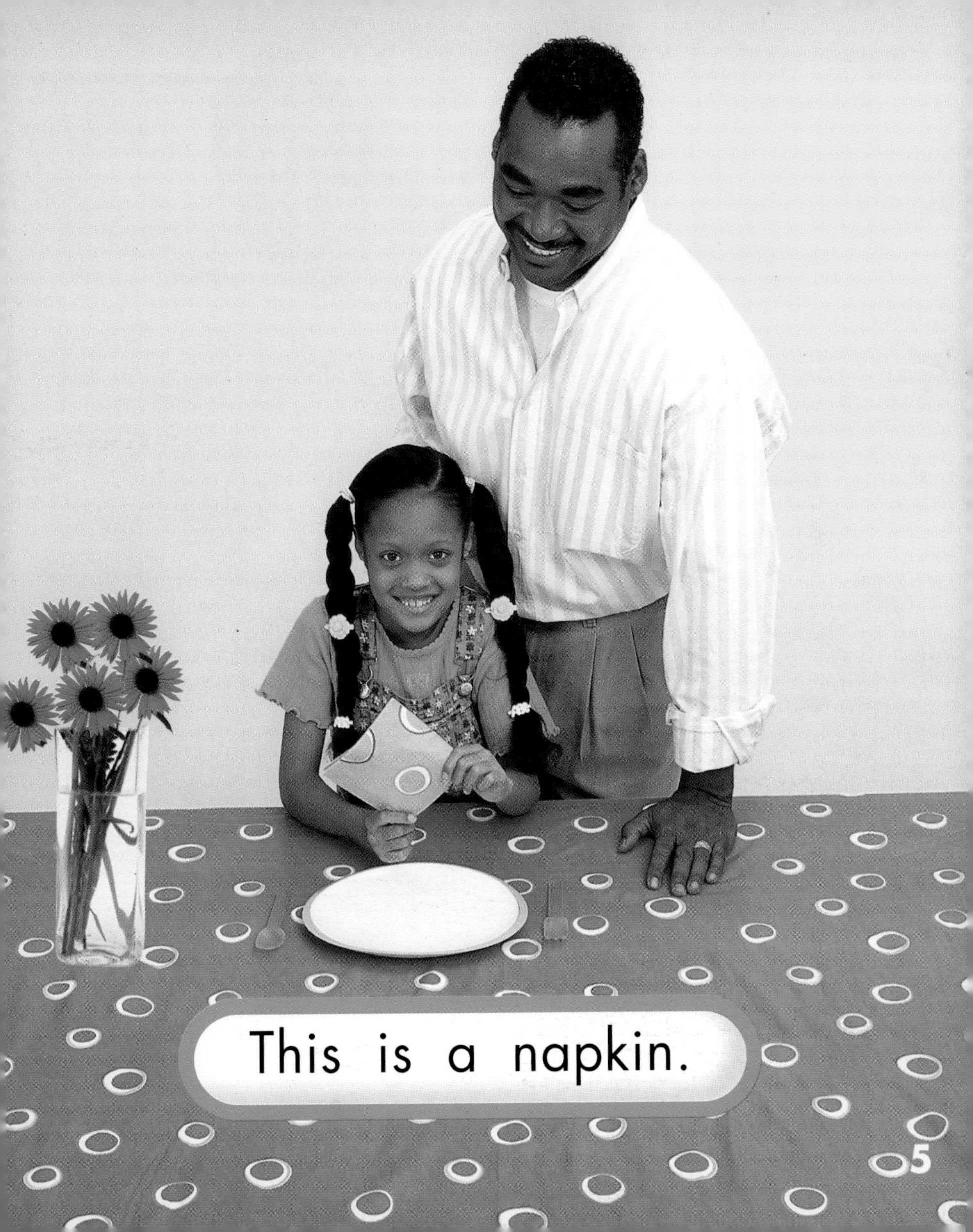

This is a napkin.

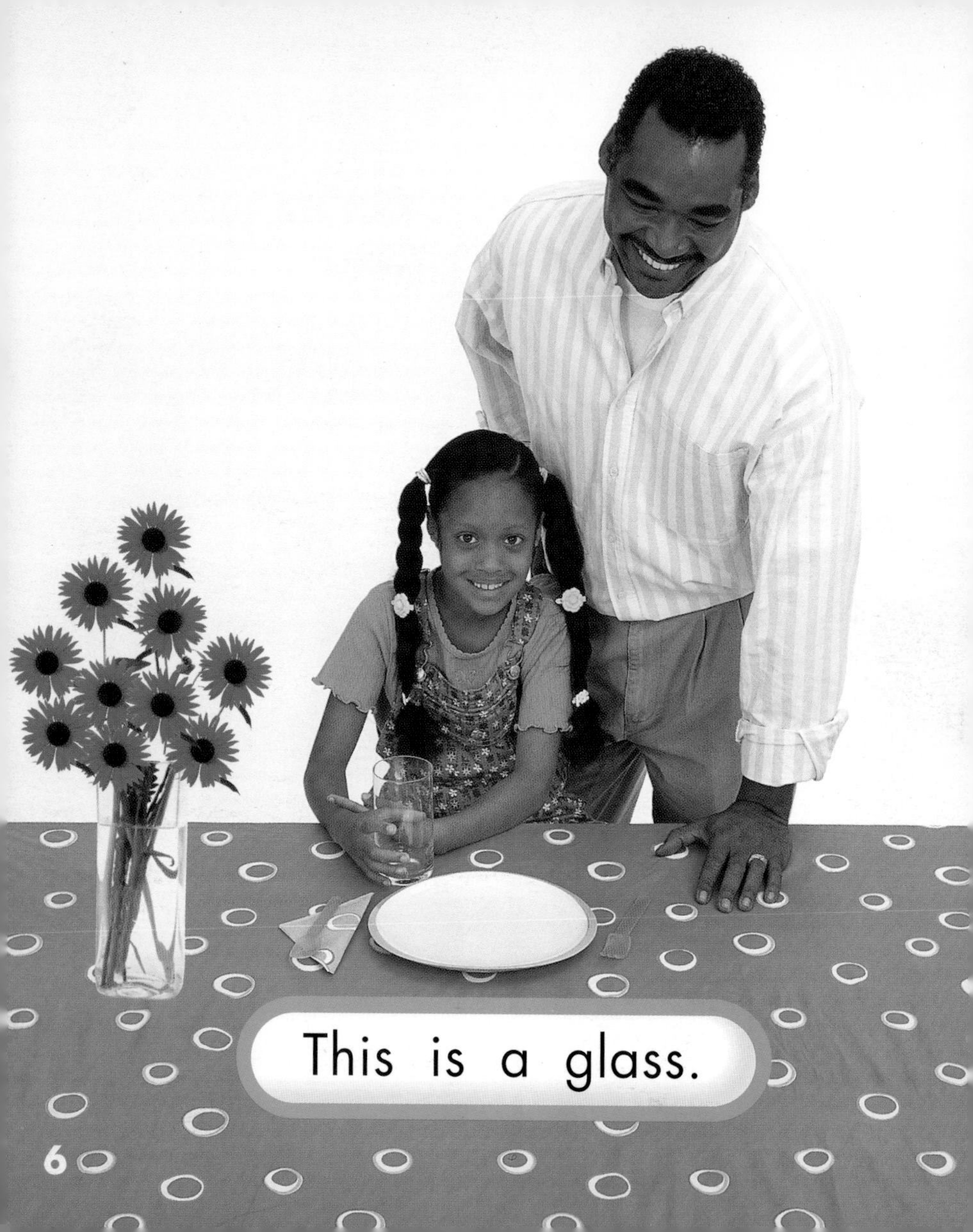

This is a glass.

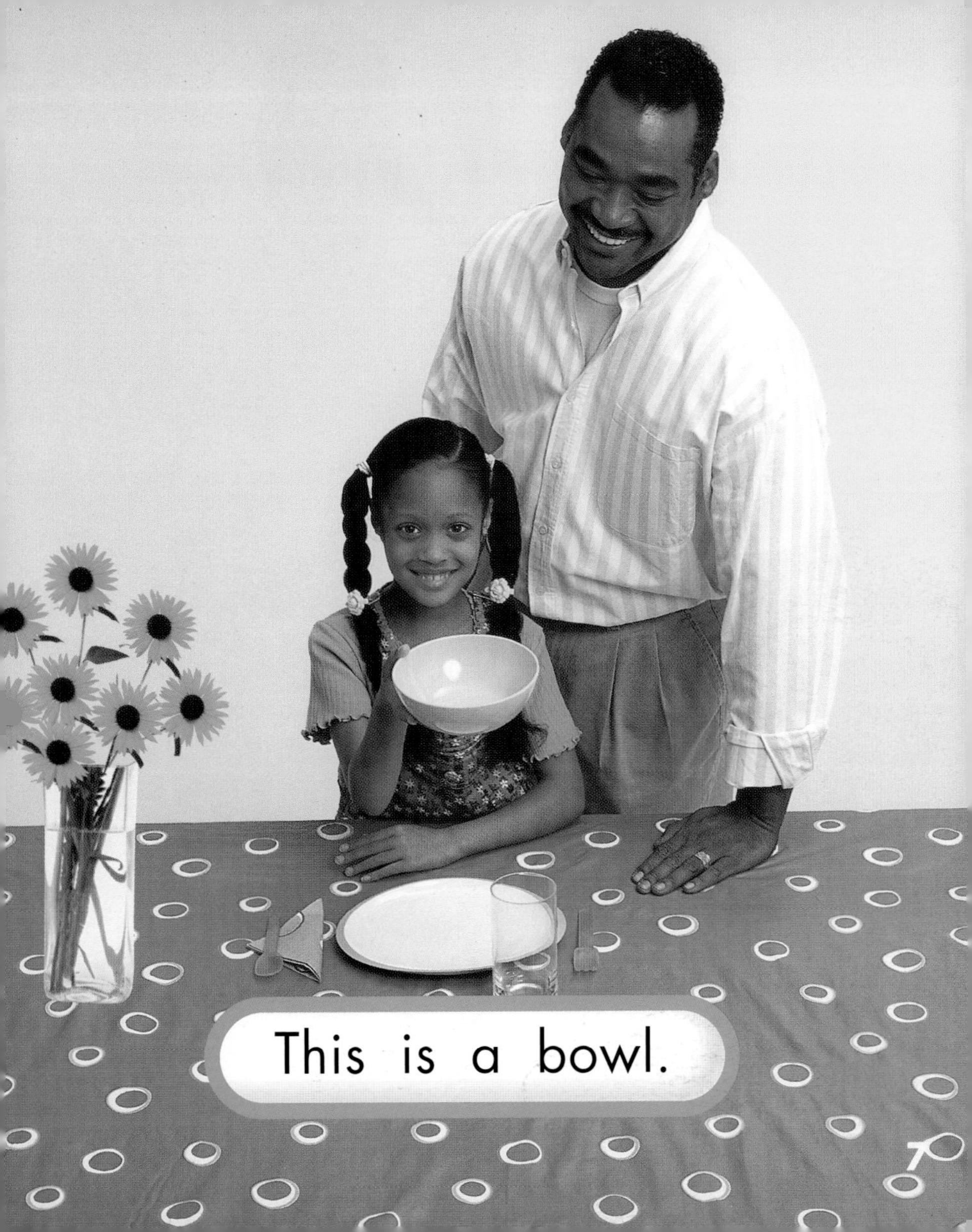

This is a bowl.

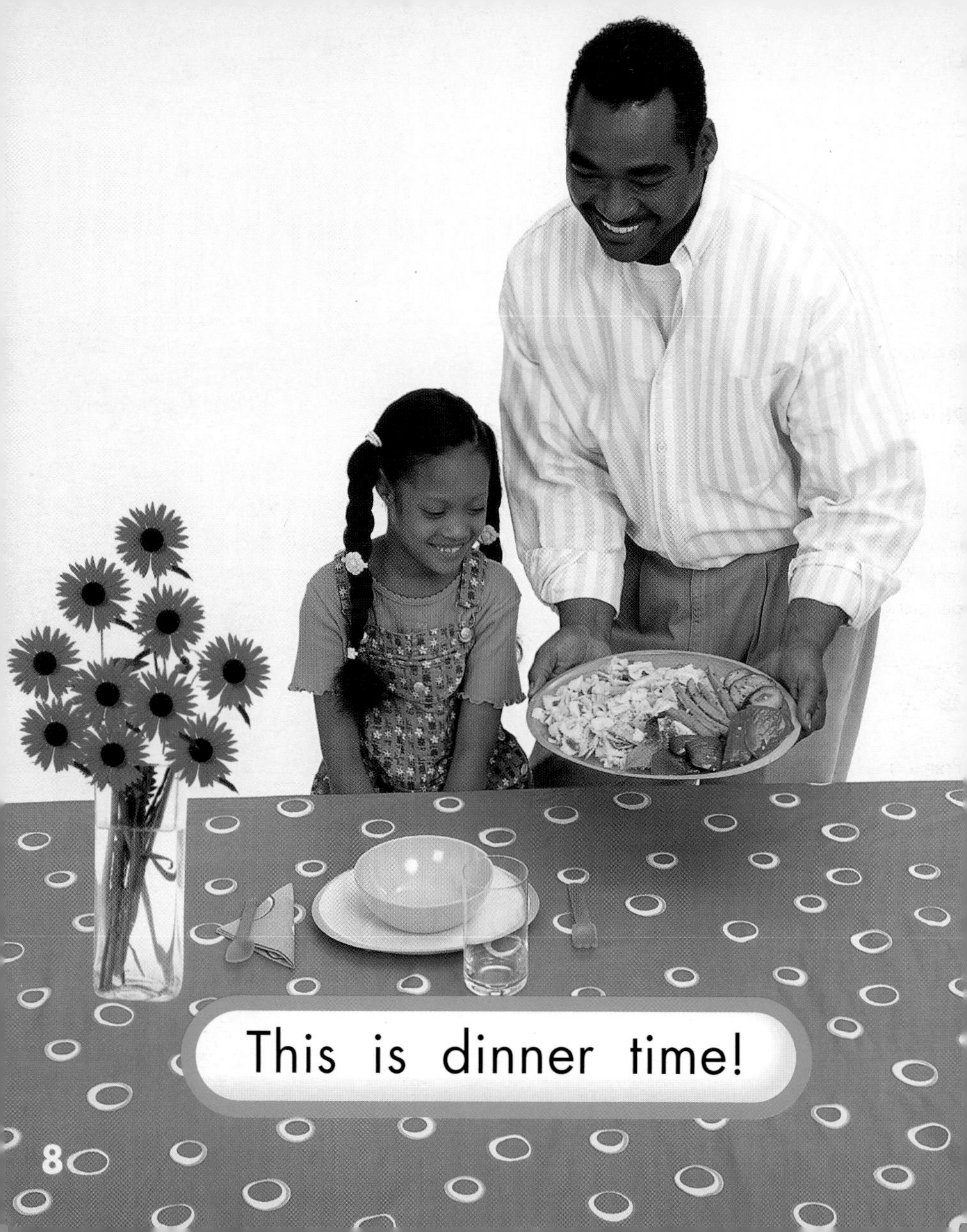

This is dinner time!